Mishi-na

Story by Joy Cowley

When the plum tree was covered
with blossom white as snow,
the boy called, "Mishi-na! Mishi-na!"
and the brown hen came running.

4

When the tree was bright green
with summer leaves,
the boy stood under it, calling,
"Mishi-na! Mishi-na!"
and the brown hen
came for her food.

When the plum tree was heavy
with ripe red plums,
the boy called the hen,
"Mishi-na! Mishi-na!"
and the brown hen
ate from his hand.

6

But in autumn,
when the leaves of the plum tree
were brown and gold,
Mishi-na went away.

The boy called and called.
No brown hen came.

The boy asked the other children,
"Have you seen my brown hen?
She has yellow feet
and very bright eyes.
She is called Mishi-na."

The other children laughed.
"Chicken soup!" they shouted.
"Your Mishi-na was made
into chicken soup!"

The boy did not believe them.

The branches of the plum tree
were bare with winter.
Still the boy called every day,
"Mishi-na! Mishi-na!"

Every day
he put out a dish of food for her.

Then, one afternoon
when the plum tree was covered
with blossom white as snow,
the boy heard a noise in the grass.